McGRAW-HILL READING

Selection Assessments

Teacher's Annotated Edition

D1313680

**McGraw-Hill
School Division**

New York • Farmington

Contents

(continued)

Book 2.2/Unit 2

Book 2.2/Unit 3

Ann's First Day

Ann's First Day

♦ Fill in the bubble next to the right answer.

Throughout these tests, you may wish to read the name of the picture aloud to identify the target sound in each phonics item.

Short a   (bat)

1.

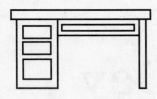

- ● sat
- ○ seat
- ○ sit
- ○ set

Say: "Look at the first picture on your page. Now look at the words next to that picture. Fill in the bubble next to the word that has the same <u>middle</u> sound as the name of the picture. "

Short e   (desk)

2.

- ○ ton
- ○ tan
- ● ten
- ○ tin

Say: "Now do the same for the rest of the pictures on your page."

Short o   (clock)

3.

- ○ hat
- ● hot
- ○ hit
- ○ hut

Short u   (sun)

4.

- ○ beg
- ○ big
- ○ bag
- ● bug

GO ON ➤

♦ Fill in the bubble next to the right answer.

Story Vocabulary

5. Most rabbits like **carrots**.
   Carrots are a kind of _____.
   - ○ animal
   - ○ house
   - ● food
   - ○ wagon

Story Vocabulary

6. Jessica's turtle **crawls**.
   Something that **crawls** _____.
   - ○ sleeps a lot
   - ○ makes loud sounds
   - ● moves slowly
   - ○ eats quickly

Story Vocabulary

7. We had to **hurry** to the bus.
   To **hurry** means to _____.
   - ● go fast
   - ○ call out
   - ○ wave
   - ○ stop

Story Vocabulary

8. Ann felt **shy** at her new school.
   Someone who is **shy** is _____.
   - ○ ready to work
   - ● afraid to meet people
   - ○ very smart
   - ○ very tired

GO ON ➤

Make Predictions

9. Ann is new at school.
   Ann's teacher will most likely _____.

   ○ get a pet for the class

   ○ yell at Ann for being late

   ○ send Robbie to another school

   ● tell the class Ann's name

Make Predictions

10. If Robbie stays at Ann's new school, then he will be _____.

   ● happy

   ○ sad

   ○ afraid

   ○ bad

Henry and Mudge

Henry and Mudge

♦ Fill in the bubble next to the right answer.

Long i: i_e   (five)

1.

Say: "Look at the first picture on your page. Fill in the bubble next to the word that has the same <u>middle</u> sound as the name of the picture."

5

- ○ rude
- ● ride
- ○ read
- ○ rid

Long o: o_e   (soap)

2.

Say: "Now do the same for the rest of the pictures on your page."

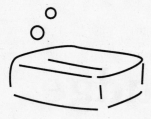

- ● bone
- ○ bean
- ○ bun
- ○ bin

Long a: a_e   (rake)

3.

- ○ some
- ○ seem
- ● same
- ○ soon

Long u: u_e   (mule)

4.

- ○ cut
- ● cute
- ○ cane
- ○ cone

GO ON ➡

♦ Fill in the bubble next to the right answer.

Story Vocabulary

5. Henry **searched** for his dog.
   When he **searched**, he _____ the dog.
   - ● looked for
   - ○ played with
   - ○ gave food to
   - ○ walked away from

Story Vocabulary

6. Henry looked at many **different** dogs.
   The dogs were **different**, so they were _____.
   - ○ all very big
   - ● not the same
   - ○ all alone
   - ○ just like Mudge

Story Vocabulary

7. Mudge **weighed** a lot.
   If he **weighed** a lot, he was _____.
   - ○ sad
   - ○ short
   - ● heavy
   - ○ hungry

Story Vocabulary

8. Henry used to **worry** and feel afraid.
   To **worry** is to be _____.
   - ● upset by something
   - ○ happy about something
   - ○ interested in something
   - ○ mad at something

GO ON ➤

Make Predictions

9. If Mudge did not walk to school with Henry, then Henry would _____.

- ○ be glad
- ○ go with friends
- ● feel afraid
- ○ take the bus

Make Predictions

10. Now that Henry and Mudge are friends, they will most likely _____.

- ○ move to a bigger house
- ● have lots of fun together
- ○ catch many ghosts
- ○ chase Henry's parents

10

Luka's Quilt

Luka's Quilt

♦ Fill in the bubble next to the right answer.

Long a: ai   (train)

1.

○ lad

○ lid

● laid

○ led

Say: "Look at the first picture on your page. Now look at the words next to that picture. Fill in the bubble next to the word that has the same <u>middle</u> sound as the name of the picture."

Long e: ea   (feet)

2.

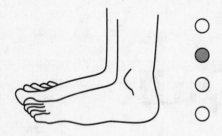

○ man

● mean

○ mine

○ moon

Say: "Now do the same for the rest of the pictures on your page."

Long e: ee   (teeth)

3.

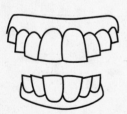

○ shout

○ shot

○ shut

● sheet

GO ON ➡

Name _____ Date _____

◆ Fill in the bubble next to the right answer.

Story Vocabulary

4. Tutu dreamed about a **garden**.
A **garden** is a place where _____.

- ○ you sleep
- ● flowers grow
- ○ cakes are made
- ○ fish swim

Story Vocabulary

5. Luka got an **idea** at the festival. An **idea** is _____.

- ○ a place you stay
- ● something that you think
- ○ something that you buy
- ○ a new friend

Story Vocabulary

6. Do you **remember** what you had for lunch?
To **remember** something is to _____.

- ● think of it again
- ○ give it away
- ○ show it to others
- ○ try to get more of it

Story Vocabulary

7. Tutu had to do some **serious** work.
Work that is **serious** is _____.

- ○ not interesting
- ○ easy
- ● not funny
- ○ outside

GO ON ➡

Story Elements: Character, Plot

8. Luka cried when she saw _____.

   ● the white flowers

   ○ many colors of flowers

   ○ her grandmother in the park

   ○ the pretty boxes

Story Elements: Character, Plot

9. Tutu used only two colors on the quilt _____.

   ○ because she only liked green

   ○ because she ran out of colors

   ● to follow the Island ways

   ○ to play a trick on Luka

Story Elements: Character, Plot

10. When Luka made something her own way, she _____.

    ○ thought it looked funny

    ● no longer felt angry

    ○ felt tired and sad

    ○ did not really like it

The Roundup
at
Rio Ranch

The Roundup at Rio Ranch

♦ Fill in the bubble next to the right answer.

Long o: oa   *(toes)*

1.

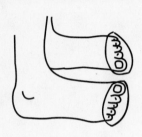

- ● boat
- ○ bite
- ○ bit
- ○ boot

Say: "Look at the first picture on your page. Now look at the words next to that picture. Fill in the bubble next to the word that has the same <u>middle</u> sound as the name of the picture."

Long i: i_e   *(smile)*

2.

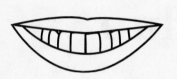

- ○ hid
- ○ had
- ● hide
- ○ hold

Say: "Now do the same for the rest of the pictures on your page."

Long i: igh   *(kite)*

3.

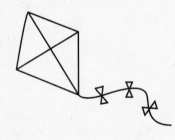

- ○ let
- ○ lit
- ○ lot
- ● light

Long o: ow   *(bows)*

4.

- ○ green
- ● grown
- ○ grain
- ○ grin

GO ON ➡

♦ Fill in the bubble next to the right answer.

Story Vocabulary

5. The men picked up the animal **carefully**.
When doing something **carefully**, you _____.

- ○ go as fast as you can
- ○ teach other people
- ● try not to make a mistake
- ○ do two things at one time

Story Vocabulary

6. The **cattle** eat grass in the field.
The **cattle** are _____.

- ○ children
- ● cows
- ○ horses
- ○ cowboys

Story Vocabulary

7. José pulled the lost animal to **safety**.
To bring to **safety** means to get _____.

- ○ into a forest
- ○ down a hill
- ● away from harm
- ○ on a horse

GO ON ▶

Story Elements: Setting

8. The cows had to be moved to a new field
because they _____.

- ○ needed to be counted
- ● had eaten all the grass in one field
- ○ were lost in the brush
- ○ could not be in a bad storm

Story Elements: Character

9. The main person in this story is _____.

- ○ Grandfather
- ○ Sugar
- ○ Antonio
- ● José

Story Elements: Character

10. Grandfather was pleased that José had _____.

- ● acted like a real cowboy
- ○ saved grandfather's truck
- ○ lost a cow
- ○ roped Antonio

10

Welcome
to
a New Museum

TIME FOR KIDS Welcome to a New Museum

♦ Fill in the bubble next to the right answer.

Long i: i_e   (bike)

1.

- ● mine
- ○ main
- ○ moan
- ○ man

Say: "Look at the first picture on your page. Now look at the words next to that picture. Fill in the bubble next to the word that has the same <u>middle</u> sound as the name of the picture."

Long o: o_e   (boat)

2.

Say: "Now do the same for the rest of the pictures on your page."

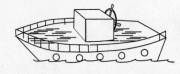

- ○ rob
- ● robe
- ○ rib
- ○ rub

Long a: a_e   (paint)

3.

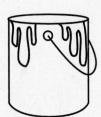

- ○ lawn
- ○ loan
- ○ line
- ● lane

Short i   (pig)

4.

- ● hit
- ○ hat
- ○ hot
- ○ hut

GO ON ➤

Name _____ Date _____

♦ Fill in the bubble next to the right answer.

Story Vocabulary

5. The **artist** has many paintings.
   An **artist** _____.
   ○ works in a shop
   ● makes beautiful things
   ○ owns lots of pets
   ○ travels around the world

Story Vocabulary

6. That painting is **famous**.
   A **famous** painting is _____.
   ○ colorful
   ○ very large
   ● well known
   ○ new

Story Vocabulary

7. It takes about one **hour** to walk through the museum.
   An **hour** is _____.
   ○ a few seconds
   ○ several days
   ○ one night
   ● sixty minutes

Story Vocabulary

8. Do you like to **visit** different places?
   When you **visit** a place, you _____.
   ● spend time there
   ○ make a picture of it
   ○ read about it
   ○ send mail there

GO ON ➤

Make Predictions

9. At the New Museum, you will likely see _____.

- ◉ a boat
- ○ farm animals
- ○ a painting by your art teacher
- ○ your picture

Make Predictions

10. When Katrina and Frederick grow up, they will likely _____.

- ○ forget all about the museum
- ○ not go back to the museum
- ○ take their work away from the museum
- ◉ take their children to see the museum

10

Lemonade for Sale

Lemonade for Sale

♦ Fill in the bubble next to the right answer.

/ü/oo   (shoe)

1.

- ● too
- ○ tea
- ○ tie
- ○ top

Say: "Look at the first picture on your page. Now look at the words next to that picture. Fill in the bubble next to the word that has the same ending sound as the name of the picture."

/ü/ew   (glue)

2.

- ○ blink
- ● blew
- ○ blow
- ○ blot

Say: "Now do the same for the rest of the pictures on your page."

/ü/ue   (zoo)

3.

- ○ club
- ● clue
- ○ clap
- ○ clay

GO ON ▶

♦ Fill in the bubble next to the right answer.

Story Vocabulary

4. "We are sold out," **announced** Sheri.
   News that is **announced** is _____.
   - ● said out loud
   - ○ kept a secret
   - ○ put on a list
   - ○ made into a joke

Story Vocabulary

5. Meg wanted a drink, but the jug was **empty**.
   An **empty** jug _____.
   - ● has nothing in it
   - ○ is too heavy
   - ○ costs lots of money
   - ○ cannot be found

Story Vocabulary

6. The ice cubes **melted** in the hot sun.
   Ice that has **melted** has _____.
   - ● turned to water
   - ○ grown bigger
   - ○ broken into pieces
   - ○ rubbed together

Story Vocabulary

7. Matthew **squeezed** six lemons for lemonade.
   When he **squeezed** the lemons, he _____.
   - ○ tossed them up
   - ● pressed them hard
   - ○ made them cold
   - ○ rolled them around

GO ON ▶

Problem and Solution

8. The club members needed money to fix their clubhouse.
They decided to _____.

- ◉ sell lemonade
- ○ make a graph
- ○ talk to the neighbors
- ○ go to the bank

Problem and Solution

9. The club members needed to keep track of their money.
Sheri decided to _____.

- ○ ask her mother
- ○ count cups
- ◉ make a graph
- ○ read a book

Problem and Solution

10. Instead of visiting the stand, people were watching Jed.
The kids asked Jed to _____.

- ○ go away
- ○ drink some lemonade
- ○ teach Meg
- ◉ move next to their stand

A Letter to Amy

A Letter to Amy

♦ Fill in the bubble next to the right answer.

1. /oi/oi   (coin)

- ○ sail
- ● soil
- ○ sell
- ○ seal

Say: "Look at the first picture on your page. Now look at the words next to that picture. Fill in the bubble next to the word that has the same <u>middle</u> sound as the name of the picture."

2. /ou/ou   (house)

- ○ shoot
- ○ sheet
- ● shout
- ○ shot

Say: "Now do the same for the rest of the pictures on your page."

3. /ow/ow   (crown)

- ○ tan
- ● town
- ○ ten
- ○ tone

4. /oi/oi   (point)

- ○ brown
- ○ bone
- ● boil
- ○ box

GO ON ➤

Name _____ Date _____

♦ Fill in the bubble next to the right answer.

Story Vocabulary

5. Peter's cake had lots of **candles**.
   The **candles** are _____.
   ○ flowers made of sugar
   ● small sticks of wax
   ○ bits of colored paper
   ○ letters made of icing

Story Vocabulary

6. The park is around the **corner**.
   A **corner** is where _____.
   ● two streets meet
   ○ children go to play
   ○ people mail letters
   ○ parties are held

Story Vocabulary

7. Mom **glanced** out the window and saw the children.
   When Mom **glanced**, she _____.
   ● looked
   ○ called
   ○ reached
   ○ jumped

Story Vocabulary

8. Amy did not hear, so the teacher **repeated** the question.
   When a question is **repeated**, it is _____.
   ○ forgotten
   ○ answered
   ● said again
   ○ written down

GO ON ▶

Problem and Solution

9. Peter wanted to invite a girl to his party.
   He was afraid of what his friends would say.
   He decided to _____.

   ○ sit down and cry

   ○ call her on the phone

   ○ draw her a picture

   ● invite her anyway

Problem and Solution

10. When the wind blew the envelope away, Peter _____

    ○ ran back to his house

    ● caught it so Amy wouldn't see it

    ○ told Willy to chase after it

    ○ got a new one at the store

10

The
Best Friends Club

The Best Friends Club

♦ Fill in the bubble next to the right answer.

/ôr/or   (door)

1.

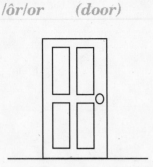

- ● tore
- ○ tire
- ○ tear
- ○ tar

Say: "Look at the first picture on your page. Now look at the words next to that picture. Fill in the bubble next to the word that has the same ending sound as the name of the picture."

/îr/ear   (deer)

2.

- ○ heat
- ○ hair
- ● hear
- ○ her

Say: "Now do the same for the rest of the pictures on your page."

/âr/are   (bear)

3.

- ○ car
- ○ core
- ● care
- ○ cure

/ôr/ore   (four)

4.

- ○ sharp
- ○ shop
- ○ share
- ● shore

GO ON ➡

Name _____ Date _____

♦ Fill in the bubble next to the right answer.

Story Vocabulary

5. Lizzie **whispered** in Harold's ear.
   When something is **whispered**, it is _____.
   - ● said quietly
   - ○ shouted
   - ○ sung
   - ○ said again

Story Vocabulary

6. Lizzie wanted to be the **president** of the club.
   The **president** is the _____.
   - ○ student
   - ○ sign maker
   - ● leader
   - ○ teacher

Story Vocabulary

7. Harold **leaned** on the porch.
   As he **leaned**, Harold _____.
   - ○ kicked at the steps
   - ● rested against the porch
   - ○ cut into the wood
   - ○ went under the steps

Story Vocabulary

8. Harold did not keep his **promise**.
   A **promise** is _____.
   - ○ a special gift
   - ● something you agree to do
   - ○ something like a club
   - ○ a very good friend

GO ON ▶

Make Inferences

9. Harold wanted Douglas to join the club because _____.

○ Lizzie was mad at him

◉ Douglas was his friend, too

○ the club was no fun

○ Douglas was a good runner

Make Inferences

10. Lizzie named the club THE NO RULES CLUB so that _____.

○ nobody could join

○ Douglas could run bases

○ Harold would cry

◉ Douglas could join

10

Jamaica Tag-Along

Name _____   Date _____

Jamaica Tag-Along

♦ Fill in the bubble next to the right answer.

/ûr/ur   (girl)

1.

- ● curl
- ○ coal
- ○ cool
- ○ Carl

Say: "Look at the first picture on your page. Now look at the words next to that picture. Fill in the bubble next to the word that has the same <u>middle</u> sound as the name of the picture."

/är/ar   (heart)

2.

- ○ firm
- ● farm
- ○ fame
- ○ foam

Say: "Now do the same for the rest of the pictures on your page."

/ûr/ir   (shirt)

3.

- ● dirt
- ○ dart
- ○ date
- ○ dent

/är/ar   (barn)

4.

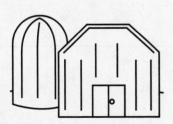

- ○ pack
- ○ pick
- ○ pork
- ● park

GO ON ➤

Name _____ Date _____

♦ Fill in the bubble next to the right answer.

Story Vocabulary

5. Jamaica hid behind the **building**.
   A **building** could be a _____.
   - ○ tree or bush
   - ● house or school
   - ○ truck or car
   - ○ wagon or cart

Story Vocabulary

6. Jamaica's friends were too **busy** to play.
   To be **busy** is to _____.
   - ○ not feel well
   - ○ be away on a trip
   - ○ be tired and bored
   - ● have lots to do

Story Vocabulary

7. Ossie used wet sand to **form** a wall.
   To **form** something is to _____.
   - ● make it
   - ○ cover it
   - ○ go through it
   - ○ wash it

Story Vocabulary

8. Berto tried to **repair** the castle.
   To **repair** something is to _____.
   - ○ hide it
   - ● fix it
   - ○ clean it
   - ○ throw it

GO ON ➤

Problem and Solution

9. Jamaica has nobody to play with, so she _____.

○ plays ball by herself

● follows Ossie

○ talks with Ossie

○ rides her bike home

Problem and Solution

10. When Jamaica sees she has hurt Berto's feelings, she _____.

○ shows him how to play ball

○ gives him a ride

● lets him help her

○ pushes him on the swing

10

Sharks

TIME **Sharks**

♦ Fill in the bubble next to the right answer.

1. /oi/oy (boy)

Say: "Look at the first picture on your page. Now look at the words next to that picture. Fill in the bubble next to the word that has the same <u>ending</u> sound as the name of the picture."

- ○ tea
- ○ tie
- ● toy
- ○ toe

2. /ôr/ore (four)

Say: "Now do the same for the rest of the pictures on your page."

- ○ star
- ○ stir
- ○ stair
- ● store

3. /är/ar (star)

- ○ tore
- ○ tire
- ○ tear
- ● tar

4. /ü/ew (shoe)

- ○ far
- ● flew
- ○ fly
- ○ fine

GO ON ➤

♦ Fill in the bubble next to the right answer.

Story Vocabulary

5. Are you **afraid** of sharks?
   If you are **afraid**, you are _____.
   - ● scared
   - ○ careful
   - ○ surprised
   - ○ proud

Story Vocabulary

6. Call for help in case of **trouble**.
   People in **trouble** _____.
   - ○ draw pictures
   - ○ read many books
   - ● have a problem
   - ○ work too hard

Story Vocabulary

7. The **lesson** about sharks was interesting.
   A **lesson** is something you _____.
   - ○ look for
   - ● learn
   - ○ put away
   - ○ play with

Story Vocabulary

8. Reading about sharks can help you **understand** them.
   To **understand** something is to _____.
   - ○ like it very much
   - ● know a lot about it
   - ○ look at it
   - ○ get pictures of it

GO ON ➤

Make Inferences

9. Sharks like to eat fish, not people. Still, people think sharks are bad. You could say that _____.

   ◉ people need to learn more about sharks

   ○ sharks like to swim with people

   ○ sharks do not eat much

   ○ people should keep sharks as pets

Make Inferences

10. We know that sharks fight sickness very well. You could say that people should _____.

    ○ try not to get sick

    ◉ get to know more about sharks

    ○ stay away from sick sharks

    ○ stop caring about sharks

10

Arthur
Writes a Story

Arthur Writes a Story

♦ Fill in the bubble next to the right answer.

Silent Letters: kn   *(nose)*

1.

Say: *"Look at the first picture on your page. Now look at the words next to that picture. Fill in the bubble next to the word that has the same <u>beginning</u> sound as the name of the picture."*

- ○ see
- ○ tree
- ○ she
- ● knee

Silent Letters: wr   *(rainbow)*

2.

Say: *"Now do the same for the rest of the pictures on your page."*

- ○ trap
- ● wrap
- ○ stop
- ○ drop

Silent Letters: kn   *(nail)*

3.

- ● knot
- ○ shot
- ○ pot
- ○ got

Silent Letters: wr   *(ring)*

4.

- ○ bright
- ○ kite
- ● write
- ○ sight

GO ON ➡

Name _____ Date _____

♦ Fill in the bubble next to the right answer.

Story Vocabulary

5. Arthur **decided** to change his story.
   When Arthur **decided**, he _____.
   ○ looked around
   ○ drew a picture
   ● made a choice
   ○ sang a song

Story Vocabulary

6. Arthur went to the **library**.
   A **library** is a place to _____.
   ○ buy food
   ● check out books
   ○ dive in
   ○ play in

Story Vocabulary

7. The class had to write about something **important**.
   When something is **important**, it _____.
   ○ makes people laugh
   ○ is hard to remember
   ● has special meaning
   ○ is not true

Story Vocabulary

8. Arthur was **proud** of his puppy Pal.
   To be **proud** of something is to _____.
   ○ be afraid of it
   ○ be worried about it
   ○ feel angry about it
   ● feel good about it

GO ON ➤

Fantasy and Reality

9. In real life, an animal like Arthur could _____.

○ write stories

○ ride a bicycle

○ go to school

● not read

Fantasy and Reality

10. The part of Arthur's story that could really happen was about _____.

○ the purple-striped elephant

● his pet business

○ living on another planet

○ floating elephants

Best Wishes, Ed

Best Wishes, Ed

♦ Fill in the bubble next to the right answer.

/ər/er   (sweater)

1.

Say: "Look at the first picture on your page. Now look at the words next to that picture. Fill in the bubble next to the word that has the same ending sound as the name of the picture."

- ○ skating
- ● skater
- ○ skated
- ○ skates

/ər/er   (letter)

2.

Say: "Now do the same for the rest of the pictures on your page."

- ○ kick
- ○ kicking
- ● kicker
- ○ kicked

/ər/er   (dancer)

3.

- ○ moving
- ○ moves
- ○ moved
- ● mover

/ər/er   (zipper)

4.

- ● baker
- ○ baking
- ○ baked
- ○ bakes

GO ON ▶

♦ Fill in the bubble next to the right answer.

Story Vocabulary

5. Ed **climbed** on the whale's back.
    When Ed **climbed**, he _____.
    ○ fell off
    ○ wrote messages on
    ● moved up
    ○ took a long nap

Story Vocabulary

6. A **couple** of birds flew by Ed.
    A **couple** is the same as _____.
    ○ hundreds
    ● two
    ○ ten
    ○ one

Story Vocabulary

7. The piece of ice **drifted** out to sea.
    When the ice **drifted**, it _____.
    ● floated away
    ○ melted
    ○ sank down
    ○ cracked

GO ON ➤

Fantasy and Reality

8. One way to tell this story is make-believe is _____.

- ○ birds are flying
- ○ a whale is swimming
- ○ Ed eats a fish
- ● Ed writes a letter

Fantasy and Reality

9. A real penguin can _____.

- ● swim in the ocean
- ○ get rides on whales
- ○ write in the snow
- ○ talk to whales

Fantasy and Reality

10. Whales cannot really _____.

- ○ swim
- ● talk
- ○ splash
- ○ eat

10

The Pony Express

The Pony Express

♦ Fill in the bubble next to the right answer.

Short e:ea   (bed)

1.

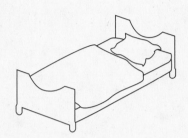

Say: "Look at the first picture on your page. Now look at the words next to that picture. Fill in the bubble next to the word that has the same <u>middle</u> sound as the name of the picture."

○ hid
○ had
● head
○ hard

Short e:ea   (bread)

2.

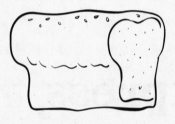

Say: "Now do the same for the rest of the pictures on your page."

● meant
○ mount
○ meet
○ mutt

Short e:ea   (thread)

3.

○ swept
○ swat
○ sweet
● sweat

Short e:ea   (shed)

4.

○ bunch
● breath
○ bring
○ braid

GO ON ▶

Name _____ Date _____

♦ Fill in the bubble next to the right answer.

5. The riders got to California **early**.
To be **early** is to be _____.

- ○ very happy
- ○ very tired
- ● sooner than planned
- ○ without any money

6. Johnnie had to **rush** to get there on time.
To **rush** is to _____.

- ○ walk away
- ○ go slowly
- ○ look for something
- ● hurry

7. Everyone agreed that the Pony Express was a great **success**.
Something that is a **success** _____.

- ● turns out well
- ○ lasts a long time
- ○ costs a lot
- ○ makes lots of people angry

GO ON ➤

Name _____ Date _____

8. Because of the Pony Express _____.

   ○ horses could carry up to 125 pounds

   ○ people wrote letters and printed newspapers

   ○ people learned to be strong and brave

   ● mail could go across the country in 10 days

9. Stopping places were built ten to twelve miles apart so that _____.

   ○ people could visit the riders

   ● horses could run at top speed between them

   ○ riders could stop for lunch

   ○ mail could be left there

10. The Pony Express ended because _____.

    ○ the riders were too tired to make the runs

    ○ the people out West no longer needed mail

    ● the new cross-country line was finished

    ○ the riders became rich

Nine-in-One, Grr! Grr!

Nine-in-One, Grr! Grr!

♦ Fill in the bubble next to the right answer.

Long e: y   (monkey)

1.

- ○ parts
- ○ parted
- ● party
- ○ parting

Say: "Look at the first picture on your page. Now look at the words next to that picture. Fill in the bubble next to the word that has the same <u>ending</u> sound as the name of the picture."

Long e: ey   (tree)

2.

- ● key
- ○ king
- ○ keep
- ○ kiss

Say: "Now do the same for the rest of the pictures on your page."

Long e: y   (turkey)

3.

- ○ ladder
- ● lady
- ○ ladle
- ○ lad

Long e: y   (money)

4.

- ○ jump
- ○ jet
- ○ jam
- ● jelly

GO ON ▶

Name _____ Date _____

♦ Fill in the bubble next to the right answer.

Story Vocabulary

5. Tiger did not want to **forget** her song.
When you **forget**, you cannot _____.
- ● remember
- ○ understand
- ○ practice
- ○ hear

Story Vocabulary

6. Tiger was **lonely** without any cubs.
To feel **lonely** is to feel that you are _____.
- ○ old and tired
- ○ very lucky
- ○ not to be harmed
- ● all by yourself

Story Vocabulary

7. "My **memory** is so bad," said Tiger.
With your **memory** you can _____.
- ● remember
- ○ go to sleep
- ○ sit down to eat
- ○ keep from falling

Story Vocabulary

8. Shao had some **wonderful** news.
Something **wonderful** is _____.
- ○ very old
- ○ funny
- ● really good
- ○ unhappy

GO ON ➤

Fantasy and Reality

9. Real tigers can _____.

- ○ ask questions of the great Shao
- ○ sail small boats
- ● climb over rocks
- ○ make up songs to help themselves remember

Fantasy and Reality

10. Something in the story that could not really happen is a _____.

- ○ bird flying high up into a tree
- ○ bird flapping its wings
- ○ tiger climbing up a hill to a cave
- ● bird telling a tiger the words to a song

Change
for the Quarter

TIME Change for the Quarter

♦ Fill in the bubble next to the right answer.

Long e: y   (cookie)

1.

○ rained

○ rains

○ raining

● rainy

Say: "Look at the first picture on your page. Now look at the words next to that picture. Fill in the bubble next to the word that has the same <u>ending</u> sound as the name of the picture."

Silent Letters: gh   (pie)

2.

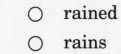

○ hill

● high

○ hay

○ hole

Say: "Now do the same for the rest of the pictures on your page."

/ər/er   (feather)

3.

● racer

○ races

○ raced

○ racing

Long e: ey   (bee)

4.

○ man

● money

○ moon

○ mine

GO ON ➡

Name _____ Date _____

♦ Fill in the bubble next to the right answer.

Story Vocabulary

5. Some people **collect** coins.
   If you **collect** things, you _____.
   - ○ weigh them
   - ● have many of them
   - ○ throw them
   - ○ have only one

Story Vocabulary

6. People can **order** coins.
   To **order** coins is to _____.
   - ● send away for them
   - ○ give them away
   - ○ talk about them
   - ○ copy them

Story Vocabulary

7. You can **join** a club and meet others who like coins.
   To **join** is to _____.
   - ○ send a note to
   - ○ write a book about
   - ○ give a speech to
   - ● become a member of

Story Vocabulary

8. People wanted to **honor** the states with new coins.
   To **honor** something is to show that you think _____.
   - ● highly of it
   - ○ it costs a lot
   - ○ it can't be used
   - ○ much time has gone by

GO ON ➤

Cause and Effect

9. Georgia was one of the first states shown on the new quarters because it _____.

○ asked to be first

○ uses more quarters than any other state

○ won a contest

● was one of the first states to join the United States

Cause and Effect

10. If many coins are collected, _____.

○ there will not be coins to go around

● more coins will be made

○ people will want more and more coins

○ no more coins will be made

Charlie Anderson

Charlie Anderson

♦ Fill in the bubble next to the right answer.

/ü/oo (foot)

1.

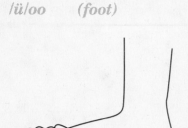

- ● look
- ○ like
- ○ lick
- ○ leak

Say: "Look at the first picture on your page. Now look at the words next to that picture. Fill in the bubble next to the word that has the same <u>middle</u> sound as the name of the picture."

/ü/oo (hook)

2.

- ○ weed
- ● wood
- ○ wade
- ○ wide

Say: "Now do the same for the rest of the pictures on your page."

/ü/oo (hood)

3.

- ● cook
- ○ cake
- ○ cart
- ○ cord

/ü/oo (book)

4.

- ○ show
- ○ short
- ○ ship
- ● shook

GO ON ➡

♦ Fill in the bubble next to the right answer.

Story Vocabulary

5. Charlie slept in the **middle** of the bed.
The **middle** is _____.

⬤ not on the end

◯ at the edge

◯ under

◯ in the back

Story Vocabulary

6. The girls **offered** Charlie some milk.
Something that is **offered** is _____.

◯ inside

◯ hidden

⬤ given

◯ lost

Story Vocabulary

7. Sarah had fun with her **clothes**.
Your **clothes** are things you _____.

◯ eat

⬤ put on

◯ grow

◯ pet

Story Vocabulary

8. Sarah heard a noise **upstairs**.
The **upstairs** is the _____.

⬤ floor over your head

◯ yard out back

◯ room where you cook

◯ room where you wash

GO ON ➤

Draw Conclusions

9. Charlie was missing, and Elizabeth stayed up all night. You know that _____.

   ○ she wanted to watch T.V.

   ● she was worried about him

   ○ her mother told her to stay up

   ○ Charlie liked milk

Draw Conclusions

10. Charlie stayed at one house in the night and at another in the day. You know that Charlie liked _____.

    ○ Elizabeth and Sarah only

    ○ chocolate-chip cookies

    ○ a house in the city

    ● the people in both houses

Fernando's Gift

Fernando's Gift

♦ Fill in the bubble next to the right answer.

Soft g   (cage)

1.

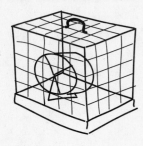

○ hug
● huge
○ hunt
○ hum

Say, "Look at the first picture on your page. Now look at the words next to that picture. Fill in the bubble next to the word that has the same <u>ending</u> sound as the name of the picture."

Soft g   (page)

2.

○ last
● large
○ lane
○ land

Say, "Now do the same for the rest of the pictures on your page."

Soft c   (mice)

3.

○ spark
○ spill
○ spin
● space

Soft c   (fence)

4.

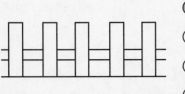

● rice
○ ripe
○ rip
○ ride

GO ON ➡

Name _____ Date _____

♦ Fill in the bubble next to the right answer.

5. The people live in a **village**.
A **village** is a small _____.

- ○ hill
- ● town
- ○ lake
- ○ house

6. Wet **soil** is good for some plants.
The **soil** is the _____.

- ○ sky
- ○ tree
- ○ bird
- ● dirt

7. The birds were very **noisy**.
Something **noisy** is _____.

- ○ pretty
- ○ long
- ○ old
- ● loud

8. The teacher **explains** forests to the class.
When the teacher **explains**, he _____.

- ● tells about
- ○ asks about
- ○ honors
- ○ goes to see

GO ON ➤

Draw Conclusions

9. Grandfather does not like the changes in the forest because he _____.

- 🔘 likes the many trees and squirrel monkeys
- ○ wants to have more trees chopped down
- ○ milks the cows and cooks
- ○ tends their crop

Draw Conclusions

10. Fernando thought Carmina was a good friend. You know this because he _____.

- ○ took her to see some flowers and animals
- 🔘 climbed trees with her and got her a gift
- ○ went with her to the city
- ○ told stories to her grandfather and to the children

10

The
Best Vacation Ever

The Best Vacation Ever

♦ Fill in the bubble next to the right answer.

/ô/au   (hawk)

1.

Say: "Look at the first picture on your page. Now look at the words next to that picture. Fill in the bubble next to the word that has the same <u>middle</u> sound as the name of the picture."

- ○ cat
- ○ coat
- ○ cot
- ● caught

/ô/aw   (yawn)

2.

Say: "Now do the same for the rest of the pictures on your page."

- ○ lane
- ○ line
- ● lawn
- ○ lean

/ô/a   (ball)

3.

- ○ take
- ○ tack
- ● talk
- ○ tuck

/ô/aw   (draw)

4.

- ○ clear
- ○ clue
- ● claw
- ○ clay

GO ON ➤

Name _____ Date _____

♦ Fill in the bubble next to the right answer.

Story Vocabulary

5. "**Guess** where I am," said Amanda.
   To **guess** is to _____.
   - ○ ride along with someone
   - ● know from clues
   - ○ wait for someone
   - ○ look at pictures

Story Vocabulary

6. Amanda wanted to **practice** her singing.
   When you **practice**, you _____.
   - ○ pay money to get something
   - ○ make a list
   - ● do something over and over
   - ○ get a job

Story Vocabulary

7. I **wonder** how the Grand Canyon was made.
   To **wonder** about something is to _____.
   - ○ be afraid of it
   - ● want to know about it
   - ○ fight over it
   - ○ want to own it

GO ON ▶

Compare and Contrast

8. Bats do not live in the Carlsbad Caverns in winter.
   Bats do live in the caverns in the _____.

   ○ spring
   ● summer
   ○ fall
   ○ night

Compare and Contrast

9. Compared to the caves Amanda saw, the Grand Canyon was _____.

   ○ darker
   ○ more crowded
   ● bigger
   ○ more fun

Compare and Contrast

10. Amanda's trip started at home and ended _____.

   ○ in Nashville
   ○ at the Grand Canyon
   ● at home
   ○ at Josie's house

10

Zipping, Zapping, Zooming Bats

Name _____ Date _____

Zipping, Zapping, Zooming Bats

♦ Fill in the bubble next to the right answer.

Digraph tch   (watch)

1.

○ can

○ cap

○ cat

● catch

Say: "Look at the first picture on your page. Now look at the words next to that picture. Fill in the bubble next to the word that has the same <u>ending</u> sound as the name of the picture."

Digraph tch   (match)

2.

○ pick

○ park

● pitch

○ pan

Say: "Now do the same for the rest of the pictures on your page."

Digraph tch   (patch)

3.

● match

○ mark

○ man

○ marsh

Digraph ph   (leaf)

4.

○ grand

● graph

○ grab

○ grasp

GO ON ➤

Name _____ Date _____

♦ Fill in the bubble next to the right answer.

5. You should not **disturb** sleeping bats.
   When you **disturb** an animal, you _____.

   ● upset it
   ○ feed it
   ○ catch it
   ○ drop it

6. **Several** caves around here are homes for bats.
   If there are **several** caves, there are _____.

   ○ a great many
   ● a few
   ○ no more
   ○ some that are hidden

7. It's fun to **explore** caves.
   To **explore** is to _____.

   ○ clean up
   ● look into closely
   ○ write stories about
   ○ block off

8. We know many **facts** about bats.
   Facts are _____.

   ○ funny stories
   ● things known to be true
   ○ things that are forgotten
   ○ old tales

GO ON ➤

Draw Conclusions

9. Bats eat insects that bite people. Bats also eat insects that eat farmer's crops. You can say that bats are _____.

   ○ fun to keep as pets

   ○ bad to have around

   ● good hunters

   ○ poor fliers

Draw Conclusions

10. Some people put bat houses in their yards. One school has a Bats Are Terrific Club. You can say that _____.

    ○ people never watch bats

    ○ many people stay away from bats

    ○ bats can't hear people move

    ● some people help bats

Going Batty for Bats

TIME FOR KIDS | Going Batty for Bats

♦ Fill in the bubble next to the right answer.

Digraph ph   *(giraffe)*

1.

Say: *"Look at the first picture on your page. Now look at the words next to that picture. Fill in the bubble next to the word that has the same <u>ending</u> sound as the name of the picture."*

- ○ gram
- ○ grab
- ○ grass
- ● graph

Soft c   *(bus)*

2.

Say: *"Now do the same for the rest of the pictures on your page."*

- ○ dash
- ● dance
- ○ dare
- ○ damp

Soft c   *(pants)*

3.

- ○ nick
- ● nice
- ○ night
- ○ nine

Soft g   *(bridge)*

4.

- ○ park
- ○ paid
- ● page
- ○ paint

GO ON ▶

♦ Fill in the bubble next to the right answer.

Story Vocabulary

5. Some people think that bats are **scary**.
Something that is **scary** is _____.

   ○ useful
   ● frightening
   ○ funny
   ○ beautiful

Story Vocabulary

6. John wants to **study** mammals.
To **study** means to _____.

   ● learn about
   ○ buy a lot of
   ○ share with
   ○ help find

Story Vocabulary

7. They **cover** their garden on cold nights.
To **cover** something is to _____.

   ○ sit in it
   ● put something over it
   ○ flatten it out
   ○ show it off to people

GO ON ▶

Compare and Contrast

8. Compared to other cities in Texas, Austin has _____.

   ● the largest number of bats

   ○ the longest caves

   ○ the most harmful mammals

   ○ the smallest bats

Compare and Contrast

9. The world's smallest mammals are _____.

   ○ insects

   ○ bumblebees

   ○ vampire bats

   ● hog-nosed bats

Compare and Contrast

10. The ones who probably do the most to help bats are _____.

    ○ people who are afraid of bats

    ○ scientists who study mammals

    ○ people who watch bats by the bridge

    ● in a club with members who like bats

The Bremen Town Musicians

The Bremen Town Musicians

♦ Fill in the bubble next to the right answer.

/âr/are   (pears)

1.

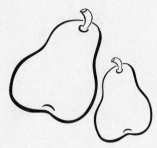

○ cooks
○ cars
○ cots
● cares

Say: "Look at the first picture on your page. Now look at the words next to that picture. Fill in the bubble next to the word that has the same <u>middle</u> sound as the name of the picture."

/ôr/or   (fork)

2.

● torn
○ turn
○ tar
○ tire

Say: "Now do the same for the rest of the pictures on your page."

/ôr/or   (corn)

3.

○ peach
○ pinch
● porch
○ perch

/ir/ear   (tears)

4.

● fears
○ forks
○ furs
○ fires

GO ON ➤

♦ Fill in the bubble next to the right answer.

Story Vocabulary

5. The farmer's **daughter** said good-bye to the dog.
    A **daughter** is a _____.
    ○ farm worker
    ◉ girl child
    ○ brother
    ○ grandfather

Story Vocabulary

6. The donkey wanted to make **music**.
    To make **music** is to _____.
    ◉ play or sing songs
    ○ draw or paint pictures
    ○ cook or bake food
    ○ write or tell stories

Story Vocabulary

7. The animals tried to **scare** the robbers.
    To **scare** is to _____.
    ○ give food
    ◉ make afraid
    ○ make laugh
    ○ show the way

GO ON ➤

Summarize

8. In the first part of the story, the donkey _____.
   - ● asks three animals to come with him
   - ○ meets three robbers with some gold
   - ○ learns how to make music
   - ○ sees a girl and her dog

Summarize

9. "The Bremen Town Musicians" is about _____.
   - ○ some robbers who live in the woods
   - ● some animals who become friends
   - ○ a house filled with gold and food
   - ○ a town called Bremen

Summarize

10. Another good title for this story might be _____.
    - ○ A Donkey, a Dog, and a Cat
    - ○ How the Animals Learned to Sing
    - ○ Three Robbers Go into a House
    - ● Four Animals and Three Robbers

Our Soccer League

Our Soccer League

♦ Fill in the bubble next to the right answer.

/ü/oo   (school)

1.

- ● root
- ○ rate
- ○ rat
- ○ rut

Say: "Look at the first picture on your page. Now look at the words next to that picture. Fill in the bubble next to the word that has the same <u>middle</u> sound as the name of the picture."

/ü/ue   (boot)

2.

- ○ sign
- ○ sun
- ● soon
- ○ seen

Say: "Now do the same for the rest of the pictures on your page."

/ü/ew   (roof)

3.

- ○ mane
- ○ man
- ○ mine
- ● moon

/ü/ew   (spoon)

4.

- ○ zaps
- ● zoom
- ○ zip
- ○ zero

GO ON ▶

Name _____ Date _____

♦ Fill in the bubble next to the right answer.

Story Vocabulary

5. The Sluggers kicked the ball across the **field**.
   The **field** is the _____.
   - ○ road
   - ○ school
   - ● playing space
   - ○ beach

Story Vocabulary

6. Everyone does their **stretches** before the game.
   When they do their **stretches**, they _____.
   - ○ eat and drink
   - ○ talk to the people
   - ● move and bend
   - ○ cheer for the team

Story Vocabulary

7. Sam **throws** the ball to Toby.
   When a player **throws** the ball, the player _____.
   - ○ kicks it softly
   - ● tosses it hard
   - ○ hits it with his head
   - ○ carries it to the goal

GO ON ➤

Summarize

8. This story tells mostly about _____.

○ how long a soccer game is and what the score is

○ what soccer players wear

○ how to be a good soccer coach

● a soccer game between the Sluggers and the Falcons

Summarize

9. In the game of soccer, the players _____.

● run around a lot

○ use a bat

○ wear masks

○ don't have much fun

Summarize

10. Another good title for the story is _____.

○ How to Win a Soccer Game

● Two Teams Play Soccer

○ Two Teams Play Baseball

○ The Score Is Tied

The
Wednesday Surprise

The Wednesday Surprise

♦ Fill in the bubble next to the right answer.

/əl/ /le/   (table)

Say: "Look at the first picture on your page. Now look at the words next to that picture. Fill in the bubble next to the word that has the same underlined ending sound as the name of the picture."

1.

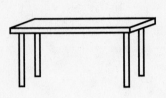

- ● bottle
- ○ batter
- ○ batch
- ○ basket

/ən/ /en/   (button)

Say: "Now do the same for the rest of the pictures on your page."

2.

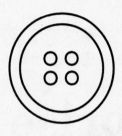

- ○ hawk
- ○ happy
- ○ hanger
- ● happen

/ər/ /er/   (hammer)

3.

- ○ broken
- ● brother
- ○ bright
- ○ breath

GO ON ➡

Name _____ Date _____

♦ Fill in the bubble next to the right answer.

Story Vocabulary

4. Mom stayed late at the **office**.
An **office** is _____.
- ○ a room for cooking
- ○ a place for running
- ○ a room for sleeping
- ● a place to work

Story Vocabulary

5. Grandma felt **nervous**.
To feel **nervous** is to be _____.
- ○ very angry
- ○ very silly
- ● a bit afraid
- ○ a bit tired

Story Vocabulary

6. Sam and Mom **wrapped** a gift for Dad.
A gift that is **wrapped** is _____.
- ● covered with paper
- ○ sent by mail
- ○ returned to the store
- ○ hidden away

Story Vocabulary

7. Grandma thought her **chance** to learn had passed.
A **chance** is a _____.
- ○ kind of school
- ● good time to do something
- ○ trip you take by yourself
- ○ special book

GO ON ➡

Sequence of Events

8. Grandma practices with Anna after _____.

- ○ Dad comes back from his trip
- ● Sam leaves for the Y
- ○ Sam returns from practice
- ○ they finish making Dad's cake

Sequence of Events

9. While Dad takes a nap, _____.

- ● Sam and Anna hang streamers in the living room
- ○ Grandma makes hot dogs and ice cream for Anna
- ○ Grandma shows everyone that she can read
- ○ Mom works at the office and Sam plays basketball

Sequence of Events

10. After Dad gets his gifts, _____.

- ○ Anna makes breath pictures on the window
- ● Grandma stands up and reads
- ○ Grandma rides the bus home
- ○ they carry Grandma's bag upstairs

10

Fossils Tell
of Long Ago

Fossils Tell of Long Ago

♦ Fill in the bubble next to the right answer.

/oi/oi   *(toys)*

1.

○ nets

○ nose

◉ noise

○ nice

Say: *"Look at the first picture on your page. Now look at the words next to that picture. Fill in the bubble next to the word that has the same <u>middle</u> sound as the name of the picture."*

/ou/ou   *(clouds)*

2.

Say: *"Now do the same for the rest of the pictures on your page."*

◉ shout

○ shoot

○ shot

○ short

/ou/ow   *(crown)*

3.

○ goal

◉ growl

○ gale

○ gill

GO ON

Name _____ Date _____

♦ Fill in the bubble next to the **right answer.**

4. Huge **creatures** lived long ago.
   Creatures are _____.
   - ● animals
   - ○ scientists
   - ○ plants
   - ○ stones

5. A **fossil** comes from another time.
   A **fossil** is a _____.
   - ○ book about the past
   - ● print or bone turned to stone
   - ○ colorful road map
   - ○ drawing on a cave wall

6. Most fossils are **buried** in the ground.
   Something that is **buried** is _____.
   - ○ filled with water
   - ● covered with earth
   - ○ broken apart
   - ○ stretched thin

7. There were **layers** of mud covering the tracks.
   The **layers** are _____.
   - ● one on top of another
   - ○ large drops or blobs of mud
   - ○ bright colors in mud
   - ○ small bits and pieces of dirt

GO ON ➡

Summarize

8. In order to form, all fossils need _____.

   ● time
   ○ bones
   ○ plants
   ○ seas

Summarize

9. All fossils are important because they show _____.

   ○ what fish did to find food
   ● what life was like at another time
   ○ why animals need mud
   ○ what people will be like in years to come

Summarize

10. Another good name for this story would be _____.

   ○ The Changing Land on Earth
   ● What We Know About Fossils
   ○ What Happened to the Big Fish?
   ○ Watch Out for Dinosaurs!

10

Are You a Fossil Fan?

Name _____ Date _____

TIME Are You a Fossil Fan?

♦ Fill in the bubble next to the right answer.

/ü/oo   (shoes)

1.

○ filled

○ fled

○ feed

● food

Say: "Look at the first picture on your page. Now look at the words next to that picture. Fill in the bubble next to the word that has the same <u>middle</u> sound as the name of the picture. "

/ou/ou   (house)

2.

○ laid

● loud

○ lad

○ lid

Say: "Now do the same for the rest of the pictures on your page."

/oi/oi   (boil)

3.

○ spell

○ spool

● spoil

○ spill

Name _____ Date _____

♦ Fill in the bubble next to the right answer.

4. After he found his first fossil, Sam's life **changed**.
When something has **changed**, it has _____.
- ● become different
- ○ been used
- ○ become better
- ○ dried up

5. Sam Girourd likes to **hunt** for clues.
To **hunt** means to _____.
- ○ read
- ● look for
- ○ talk about
- ○ remember

6. He found a few **pieces** at a time.
Pieces are _____.
- ● small bits
- ○ light marks
- ○ hard coverings
- ○ big stripes

7. You can learn about fossils in a **magazine**.
A **magazine** is most like a _____.
- ○ museum
- ○ school
- ● newspaper
- ○ show

GO ON ➤

Sequence of Events

8. As Sam glued the bits together, he _____.

- ● saw that the bits formed a dinosaur's tooth
- ○ spent hours and hours finding more tiny bones
- ○ threw the bigger bones away
- ○ went to Alabama for a visit

Sequence of Events

9. After Sam shows he is a good scientist, _____.

- ● others can hear his age
- ○ others will send him a newspaper
- ○ he will get more fossils
- ○ he will visit his grandmother

Sequence of Events

10 First Sam made a find. Then he _____.

- ○ showed it to his family
- ● wrote about it
- ○ started to collect fossils
- ○ put it back

10

Officer Buckle
and
Gloria

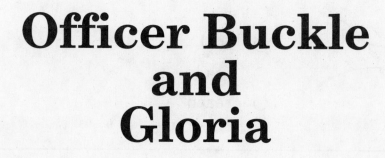

Officer Buckle and Gloria

♦ Fill in the bubble next to the right answer.

Digraph tch   (watch)

1.

- ● match
- ○ mast
- ○ man
- ○ map

Say: "Look at the first picture on your page. Now look at the words next to that picture. Fill in the bubble next to the word that has the same <u>ending</u> sound as the name of the picture."

Digraph ch   (touch)

2.

- ○ rest
- ○ real
- ○ read
- ● reach

Say: "Now do the same for the rest of the pictures on your page."

Digraph ph   (wolf)

3.

- ○ grand
- ○ grass
- ● graph
- ○ grab

GO ON ➤

Name _____ Date _____

♦ Fill in the bubble next to the right answer.

Story Vocabulary

4. The **audience** clapped for Gloria.
   The **audience** is _____.
   ○ the person speaking
   ○ the animal trainer
   ● the people who watch a show
   ○ someone who works at a school

Story Vocabulary

5. Be sure to **wipe** the table.
   To **wipe** a table is to _____.
   ○ send it away
   ● clean it off
   ○ find out about it
   ○ see how big it is

Story Vocabulary

6. People who are careless may cause **accidents**.
   When **accidents** happen _____.
   ● something breaks or people get hurt
   ○ people go to their cars
   ○ people stay in their homes
   ○ something gets lost

Story Vocabulary

7. The children **cheered** when they saw Gloria.
   When they **cheered**, they _____.
   ○ ran away
   ● shouted and clapped
   ○ woke up
   ○ sat down and stared

GO ON ▶

Form Generalizations

8. The main reason Officer Buckle shared his safety tips
was so _____.

- ○ he could go on the 10 o'clock news
- ○ Gloria would get to visit the children
- ○ children would send thank-you letters
- ● people could keep from getting hurt

Form Generalizations

9. The children liked it when Gloria came with Officer Buckle
because _____.

- ○ Officer Buckle spoke louder when Gloria was there
- ● most children like to watch dogs do tricks
- ○ Gloria knew which safety tips the children would like
- ○ Officer Buckle told jokes when Gloria was with him

Form Generalizations

10. When the people in town heard about Gloria,
they _____.

- ● wanted Officer Buckle and Gloria to visit their school
- ○ wanted to get rid of Officer Buckle
- ○ did not want to hear about safety tips anymore
- ○ put safety tips up for others to read

10

Tomás
and
the Library Lady

Tomás and the Library Lady

♦ Fill in the bubble next to the right answer.

Long e: ee   (sleep)

1.

Teacher says, "Look at the first picture on your page. Now look at the words next to that picture. Fill in the bubble next to the word that has the same <u>middle</u> sound as the name of the picture."

- ● feet
- ○ foot
- ○ fight
- ○ fit

Long e: ea   (peach)

2.

Say: "Now do the same for the rest of the pictures on your page."

- ○ bed
- ○ bud
- ○ bid
- ● bead

Long i: igh   (kite)

3.

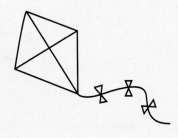

- ○ note
- ○ nest
- ● night
- ○ nut

GO ON ▶

Name _____ Date _____

♦ Fill in the bubble next to the right answer.

4. Tomás asked the lady if he could **borrow** a book.
   To **borrow** a book is to _____.
   ○ hide it in a safe place
   ● use one that belongs to another
   ○ show it to friends
   ○ ask questions about it

5. Tomás listened to his grandfather tell stories in the **evenings**.
   The **evenings** are _____.
   ○ at lunchtime
   ○ on the weekend
   ● early nighttime
   ○ when the sun comes up

6. The car drove across the **desert**.
   A **desert** is a _____.
   ● hot, dry land
   ○ busy road
   ○ rocky beach
   ○ high, steep mountain

7. The lady gave Tomás a **package**.
   A **package** is a _____.
   ○ letter
   ● bundle
   ○ pet
   ○ drink

GO ON ➡

Form Generalizations

8. The people in Tomás's family have a few jobs.
You could say they are _____.

- ● hard working
- ○ very rich
- ○ sick of Iowa
- ○ mad at each other

Form Generalizations

9. Some people like the library because they can _____.

- ○ show others they know how to read
- ● learn about interesting things
- ○ surprise the library lady
- ○ give some books to others

Form Generalizations

10. From this story, you could say that libraries are _____.

- ● friendly places
- ○ in every town
- ○ only for children
- ○ not for people who travel

10

Princess Pooh

Princess Pooh

♦ Fill in the bubble next to the right answer.

Long a:ai   (snake)

1.

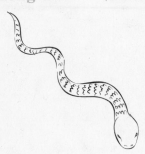

- ● chain
- ○ choice
- ○ chew
- ○ champ

Say: "Look at the first picture on your page. Now look at the words next to that picture. Fill in the bubble next to the word that has the same middle sound as the name of the picture."

Long o: oa   (boat)

2.

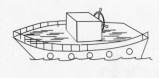

- ○ raid
- ○ ride
- ○ red
- ● road

Say: "Now do the same for the rest of the pictures on your page."

Long a: a_e   (plate)

3.

- ○ book
- ● bake
- ○ bike
- ○ beak

GO ON ▶

Name _____ Date _____

♦ Fill in the bubble next to the right answer.

Story Vocabulary

4. Penny was treated like a **princess**.
   A **princess** is a _____.
   ○ worker in a camp
   ○ very young child
   ● daughter of a king or queen
   ○ servant in a castle

Story Vocabulary

5. Patty's **cousins** came for a visit.
   Her **cousins** are _____.
   ○ people next door
   ● her aunt's children
   ○ children at school
   ○ her parents' friends

Story Vocabulary

6. Patty went to a **restaurant**.
   A **restaurant** is a place that _____.
   ○ sells books
   ● serves food
   ○ shows movies
   ○ lends money

Story Vocabulary

7. The people **crowded** around the wheelchair.
   When people **crowded**, they _____.
   ○ danced and sang
   ○ spoke quietly
   ● moved close together
   ○ hunted and hunted

GO ON ➤

Main Idea

8. This story is about Patty Jean learning _____.

- ● how her sister feels
- ○ to ride across the street
- ○ what her parents do
- ○ to carry packages

Main Idea

9. Patty Jean learns that being in a wheelchair is not easy. She learns this when _____.

- ○ a baseball player helps her
- ○ Penny takes her for a ride
- ○ the wheels turn faster
- ● the wheels sink and stop

Main Idea

10. The sisters' talk at bedtime makes Patty Jean think _____.

- ○ she should have her own wheelchair
- ○ Penny should teach her how to use the wheelchair
- ● Princess is not a good name for her sister
- ○ she should have her own bedroom

Swimmy

Swimmy

♦ Fill in the bubble next to the right answer.

Soft g   *(cage)*

1.

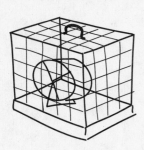

- ● page
- ○ pay
- ○ paid
- ○ paint

Say: "Look at the first picture on your page. Now look at the words next to that picture. Fill in the bubble next to the word that has the same ending sound as the name of the picture."

Soft g   *(stage)*

2.

- ○ chain
- ○ chance
- ● change
- ○ champ

Say: "Now do the same for the rest of the pictures on your page."

Soft c   *(ice)*

3.

- ○ fade
- ○ fair
- ○ fake
- ● face

Soft c   *(mouse)*

4.

- ○ knife
- ● nice
- ○ night
- ○ nine

GO ON ➤

Name _____ Date _____

♦ Fill in the bubble next to the right answer.

Story Vocabulary

5. The tiny fish **escaped** from the big fish.
When the fish **escaped**, he _____.

- ○ fell behind
- ● got away
- ○ went again
- ○ turned around

Story Vocabulary

6. Swimmy was **hidden** by the big rock.
To be **hidden** is to be _____.

- ● kept out of sight
- ○ badly hurt
- ○ carried far away
- ○ made to look big

Story Vocabulary

7. The big fish looked **fierce**.
To be **fierce** is to _____.

- ○ be sad
- ○ act silly
- ● be scary
- ○ act worried

Story Vocabulary

8. If trees are **swaying**, they are _____.

- ○ growing very close together
- ● moving gently back and forth
- ○ touching the ground
- ○ bending toward the sun

GO ON ▶

Form Generalizations

9. For a while, Swimmy swam by himself.
   Then he was glad to join a school of fish.
   You could say that _____.

   ● it is no fun being alone all the time

   ○ it is nice to swim in the sea

   ○ most fish swim only by themselves

   ○ all little fish swim in big groups

Form Generalizations

10. First the small fish were afraid and hid.
    Then Swimmy taught them how to swim as a group.
    You could say that _____.

    ○ everyone should learn how to swim

    ○ it is better to swim alone

    ○ small fish should always stay hidden

    ● working together makes good things happen

10

The World's Plants Are in Danger

TIME FOR KIDS The World's Plants Are in Danger

♦ Fill in the bubble next to the right answer.

Long o : ow   (bowl)

1.

- ○ grain
- ● grown
- ○ grin
- ○ green

Say: "Look at the first picture on your page. Now look at the words next to that picture. Fill in the bubble next to the word that has the same <u>middle</u> sound as the name of the picture."

Long i : igh   (write)

2.

- ○ neat
- ○ not
- ○ nip
- ● night

Say: "Now do the same for the rest of the pictures on your page."

Long e : ea   (meal)

3.

- ● bean
- ○ bet
- ○ bows
- ○ band

Long i: i_e   (slide)

4.

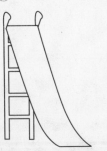

- ○ tame
- ● time
- ○ tin
- ○ tan

GO ON ➤

♦ Fill in the bubble next to the right answer.

Story Vocabulary

5. The farmers **cleared** the land.
    Land that has been **cleared** is land where _____.
    - ● trees and plants have been taken away
    - ○ rows of wildflowers have been planted
    - ○ no deep holes have been dug
    - ○ animals have been sent to live

Story Vocabulary

6. Some types of trees may soon **disappear**.
    To **disappear** is to _____.
    - ○ grow to be tall
    - ● go away forever
    - ○ be switched
    - ○ stay the same

Story Vocabulary

7. They must **warn** those children not to pick the wildflowers.
    To **warn** the children is to _____.
    - ○ pay them money
    - ○ have a fight with them
    - ○ show them how
    - ● tell them ahead of time

GO ON ▶

Main Idea

8. This story is mostly about _____.
   - ○ palm trees, roses, and lilies
   - ○ the world's largest flower
   - ◉ harm to plants, trees, and flowers
   - ○ the building of roads and factories

Main Idea

9. Plants are in trouble _____.
   - ○ in California
   - ○ in forests only
   - ○ in parks and forests
   - ◉ all over the world

Main Idea

10. Plants and trees disappear when _____.
    - ◉ people build roads and factories
    - ○ animals use them for food
    - ○ people forget to feed them
    - ○ the days and nights are too hot

10

McGraw-Hill Reading
Selection Assessments: Student Record Chart

Name _____

Unit	Story Title	Phonics		Vocabulary	Comprehension		Total
BOOK 2.1/Unit 1	Ann's First Day	Short Vowels (a, e, o, u)	4	4	Make Predictions	2	10
	Henry and Mudge	Long i: i_e Long o: o_e Long a: a_e Long u: u_e	4	4	Make Predictions	2	10
	Luka's Quilt	Long a: ai Long e: ea Long e: ee	3	4	Story Elements: Character, Plot	3	10
	The Roundup at Rio Ranch	Long o: oa Long i: i_e, igh Long o: ow	4	3	Story Elements: Setting, Character	3	10
	Welcome to a New Museum	Long i: i_e Long o: o_e Long a: a_e Short i	4	4	Make Predictions	2	10
BOOK 2.1/Unit 2	Lemonade for Sale	/ü/ oo, ew, ue	3	4	Problem and Solution	3	10
	A Letter to Amy	/ oi / oi / ou / ou, ow	4	4	Problem and Solution	2	10
	The Best Friends Club	/ ôr / or, ore / îr / ear / âr / are	4	4	Make Inferences	2	10
	Jamaica Tag-Along	/ ûr / ur, ir / är / ar	4	4	Problem and Solution	2	10
	Sharks	/ oi / oy / ôr / ore / är / ar / ü / ew	4	4	Make Inferences	2	10
BOOK 2.1/Unit 3	Arthur Writes a Story	Silent Letters: kn, wr	4	4	Fantasy and Reality	2	10
	Best Wishes, Ed	/ər/ er	4	3	Fantasy and Reality	3	10
	The Pony Express	Short e: ea	4	3	Cause and Effect	3	10
	Nine-in-One, Grr! Grr!	Long e: y, ey	4	4	Fantasy and Reality	2	10
	Change for the Quarter	Long e: y, ey Silent Letters: gh /ər/ er	4	4	Cause and Effect	2	10

Name _____

Unit	Story Title	Phonics	Vocabulary	Comprehension	Total
BOOK 2.2/Unit 1	Charlie Anderson	/ ŭ / oo	4 / 4	Draw Conclusions / 2	10
	Fernando's Gift	Soft g Soft c	4 / 4	Draw Conclusions / 2	10
	The Best Vacation Ever	/ ô /au, aw, a	4 / 3	Compare and Contrast / 3	10
	Zipping, Zapping, Zooming Bats	Digraphs tch, ph	4 / 4	Draw Conclusions / 2	10
	Going Batty for Bats	Digraph ph Soft c Soft g	4 / 3	Compare and Contrast / 3	10
BOOK 2.2/Unit 2	The Bremen Town Musicians	/ âr / are / ôr / or / îr / ear	4 / 3	Summarize / 3	10
	Our Soccer League	/ ü / oo, ue, ew	4 / 3	Summarize / 3	10
	The Wednesday Surprise	/əl/ le /ən/ en /ər/ er	3 / 4	Sequence of Events / 3	10
	Fossils Tell of Long Ago	/ oi / oi / ou / ou, ow	3 / 4	Summarize / 3	10
	Are You a Fossil Fan?	/ ü / oo / ou / ou / oi / oi	3 / 4	Sequence of Events / 3	10
BOOK 2.2/Unit 3	Officer Buckle and Gloria	Digraphs ph, tch, ch	3 / 4	Form Generalizations / 3	1
	Tomás and the Library Lady	Long e: ee, ea Long i: igh	3 / 4	Form Generalizations / 3	1
	Princess Pooh	Long a: ai, a_e Long o: oa	3 / 4	Main Idea / 3	1
	Swimmy	Soft g Soft c	4 / 4	Form Generalizations / 2	1
	The World's Plants Are in Danger	Long o: ow Long i: igh, i_e Long e: ea	4 / 3	Main Idea / 3	1